KB075734

Under there mountain

김용호 지음

Contents list underline.

1.Light up boys and girls.

2.Be meet children.

3.Let us go there.

4.We gather in my house to be planning to go to the mountain.

5.Only their adventure is starting with us.

under there mountain...

This is story is nonfiction about one's children of adventure.

1. Light up boys and girls

Shining on the playground, be variety children to playing.

One is wearing red shirt and other is wearing blue pants doing playing with each other talking about one's pride of putting shoes, other that is going up the play stair and the others is playing soccer with each other wearing uniform, and ground left corner is one girls is sitting with wearing skirt be half folding, next is two's boys drawing paint on the ground one is pick up stick and other is have thin and little long be able painting stone. Two is sitting on the front of cement stand one is painting is small one grade house and another is painting is small animal.

One is question to the other.

We do not tell each other name!

what your name?

nearly done sitting boy was little long have no comment after he told me.

Well, could you have calling smith? John smith!

My mom's name is smith catherine and my father is miller smith.

'It is my parent's first names have doing collected the head noun.' And my name is that.

After the boy is the told quietly drawing had seeing on the ground with graphs small stone and done smiling oneself.

After moment, that boy had done questions is speaking to him.

My name is fish jonidan!

My father is jonidan Eric, he is speaking with rise tone to the boy. Because surrounded is noise in the ground.

John! How about the painting? I am sincerely question to him.

He is sending slice smiling to me and answering.

The painting is small house with one grade stair has aside stand by one man.

You are very ability!

I am seeing aside on sitting down.

What is this? He is moment thinking in and speaking to me.

It is my mind. I am thinking that variety forms are that I am painting that is cycle, triangle, and angle. That in is beautiful present, future.!

That painting is thinking variety hope to me. He speak to me kindly, gently.

Going up little accent windy side staying us. Because we had drawing painting has nearly disappeared with windy.

We both little fail but we are happy because we have made friend each other,

we are going around side on ground with often running and walking,

in the sky is shiny to us and in ground is little worm. I am questions to him.

How about you for meal? Meal sold unbelievably delicious that.

I am carefully request to him.

Fish has moment thinking about that. And speaking to me.

I want to meal, but I have no money, with concern that.

He his two hands get in the pocket. and side two's hand rise middle of body and has swing, with full of concerns.

I am smile to him and speaking to him with smiling.

Do not care of that! I have money that enough buy the me.!

Fish is smiling to me,

Let us go mile store! Fish was please then little before right time.

We do hand each other going to the store.

Then arriving the store. Being crowd with peoples, on my hand is little more money to buy meal.

Hi boss! Could you help me buy the meal?

Of course! What kind could have meal?

I am little moment. And speaking to

boss.

I am like ordering milk and bread each two. Please?

The boss is pleased to me. milk is ten hundred won, bread is twenty hundred won!

Fish! How about you buy that?

Whatever is ok to me!

I am taking out that in my pocket. And pass to boss. And I milk and bread send him.

We have bow to boss, and we do

carry to milk and bread, to the garden. Garden planted as woods. That seen to me the in garden. The garden in out line is bench to made of wood.

The bench made of done painted old wood.

We breath fresh air thorough aisle cover with woods as walking.

We are sitting on the bench, and then lift my meal tie with bend and I have eaten.

Surround is many people is in garden.

He is carefully taking out meal in my case is in small pack.

At west slice windy come to me be booming

I am taking out meal and question to him,

How about your meal?

That is good for me. He is speaking to me as eating meals.

It is delicious the bread is cooking fried doing as plant oil. And very sweetly.

We have all sums.

Worm sunshine come here us in mind do as doing shade of wood. We have walking for moment around.

Fish! How about you are going my home. I am carefully request visiting my home. He is thinking about moment,

Yes! I do that! John!

I am please receiving that.

We grape each other left hand and right hand and walk side street.

How long over there and you get in reached your home? Fish is question to me with in and out breath.

Maybe left twenty minutes! I am doing clearance response.

We as soon as walking forward to ahead is seeing sun. the sun is along with going for us.

On the street is plant as red color's cement stone is loose bright change lightly dark red been change. Side load is standing electronic light .as yet out is brightly has be off.

Also, fishes have question me. About family number.

I am responsible to question that,

My family is five. Parents, elder brother, grandmother.

I am question to fish.

How many numbers is your family?

Fish is answering that question kindly.

My family is parents, elder sister, me are four.

We have each other smiling with us.

As soon as walking, seen to me my

blue color's shoes was being cover to dusty of ground. So do Fish's shoes, we walk to my house as much victory soldier going in, side street is lining woods, that lately spring season's beautiful pride for me, in the air is blooming sweetly and fresh. Going into my noise.

Nearly reach my home then fish is question me.

John! Who is in your house?

May be my mom is in!

My brother was going to school and

my father was going company. John is answer with smiling for him.

How long staying your home.?

May be as your thinking.!

John's house roof is on brightly by directly sunshine, house's around is full as green plant. The house near is white color's doghouse.

Hi! John! How many dogs is in.?

It is three!

One is two old female and other is male, last is puppy.

Original seven is, but six was that my mom sold to neighborhoods.

I am open little half wear white's color's front door, and I am calling my mom,

Hello! Mom! I am going in and with my friend!

John! Go in?

Yes! Mom!

Where are you join? Mom is carefully question to us.

We are meet at playground in school.

Could you help me john?

How do you help that?

Today is go in my house with your friend because I must cook more than meal we have before,

Could you wash hands, and go in kitchen?

My friend fish have browser with me in my house,

And fish washes hand and face in my bathroom and I am running to my mom, mom reserves plus menu are bread, soup, and vegetable,

May I help you?

Ok! do get that. Mom passes me meal on the cooking desk.

 I am getting it. And that set on the table.

Meal is near reserved I am calling my friend.

Hi! Fish could you have dinner!

I am cry to my room. Fish has directly come here.

Hi sir! fish has bow her!

Two is sitting each other her front of line.

Have a delicious! My gentlemen!

Mom is speaking to them with widely sounds.

Fish is smile to her,

Yes! Sir.!

I and he are taking it. Carefully,

One bread is piece and go in the mouth, and milk is little that going in my mouths,

My mom is seeing lastly my friend is

fish.

My mom is question to him about family.

Hi fish! what is your old?

May be seven old! Fish is answer about that.

Your old is little one old than my son! But the old can be friend with each other.

After John and I have a meal, go in the bathroom, and brush teeth and go in my bathroom.

We have speaking with about books.

Then I am going to school about two grades, but fish is now one grade.

Fish questions about study.

My book is easy, but john! Your book is little difficult studying to me.

Fish! Could you have talking stopping that?

Could you we are go to the out and have playing soccer.?

Ok!

I am taking boll room in the corner

and go out with fish.

John's house's front yard is little widely to me.

John do hit the ball to him, as soon as fish is receiving the ball. And the boll does hit by fish foots. The boll rolling to his house wall and, the boll coming once more john's foot.

John and fish each other is serving and receiving the boll.

Hi! John!

Please! Pass me boll here! More Fastly.

John breath is rising over noise. But he is involve hitting boll.

Fish! Drawing left! I am running left. And I receive boll that fish passing to me. One more going right and receive the boll and pass that to him. Fish and I are in deep the playing.

John's face is fully wetted by playing, we moment rest side house' well.

Fish! Are you have water? I am carefully questions him.

Ok!

I am going to kitchen, picking up water bottle, and send him.

Water is cooling because I and him 's mind is very clearly.

Fish is smiling to me, have speaking,

Today is very wonderful day!

Let us have always this playing!

Fish and I going in the house and into the bathroom. Wash the body, in orderly.

Mom?

Why? John?

Maybe. Fish will back home!

All right has carefully gone! fish!

Yes. Sir. fish is responsible that, and he is running his home.

Night is approach in the dark. I am farewell to my mom, and

Going in the sleeping. Night in the sky is brightly more than anymore that.

John! wake up! My mom is calling for me.

I have getting up on the bed by mom's sounds, I am directly going to bathroom and wash face, hand.

My brother is yet in the dream.

I go to the kitchen and drinking milk and going out.

Outside is clear. Still come here darkness. In the sky is red and dark is more than more spray is disappeared by rising sunshine,

I am exerciser with my football. My right foot is pass on my left that. I am running to around with my head foot doing be on ball.

Dawn's air is very fresh to me.

My in mouth is setting my singing sounds with breath.

I am going to my house. my mother is kitchen, and my brother is wake up then.

My brother is name is pitter smith!

My brother is always lately wake up in the morning.

I am going my bathroom, and I am ordering room. My brother and I are stay on same room, my brother wash face after going to the kitchen with me and my father is already wake up and carry of cows.

Mom is doing cooking for us. Brother and I are going for dish and have meal with father.

When we have meal with together. We have prayed to family. And my father is ahead meal and following have end meal my brother is going to room and to go to the school my brother is orderly bookbag and directly to the school. My brother is four degreed.

Mom, I am going now!

Well, have carefully doing sight!

So do I rise up the chair.

I am going to my bathroom. Brush my teethes. And I am going my house back yard. The yard is very peacefully. Because

Windy is blowing to the yard slowly.

I am down going to nearly country, the road is tractor is nearly can passing.

sometime on load some people was passing me, then I am asking to the person.

could you help me?

I am going the grocery store. I have needed to buy candy!

Passed one person is approach to me and speaking to me,

How need I help your aid?

Hi! I have to going to grocery store under country! The person is kindly speaking to me,

No problem! Guide!

I have telling you about that.

Thank you for the direct the point! I

am seeing and speaking to the person.

Could you listen to my direct?

Firstly, if you have to going to following this road with about three hundred miter and you will be seeming two load line, then going to follow the left line, if at there you have to one hundred, you will see the country. Then one more question to the person.

Thank you very much for give me direction. sir!

I am farewell, and I am going to the

country.

As He told me, I was going to the destination, I am on walk is roadside is beautiful yellow flower growing and anyway I go to there, it is booming leaf on the ground.

I am walk for fifty minutes then I am seeing the divided roads.

As the person told me, I am going to left road. Sometime some people passing me, about twenty miter I am going to, I am seeing side road near currenting narrow water.

I am going directly to the country.

After moments, I had reached that, there were many people,

Maybe the country's festival will be opening.

In the square is street vendors, and musical band, so on...

I am asking the passing the person.

Could you help me. sir?

The gentleman is answering my question,

no problem!

Could you tell me? Where was I going to the grocery store?

The person is changing face to the little red.

I am sorry, I am here first!

The man disconcerted with smiling.

Thank you, sir!

I am standing on square longtime, and one more time question the person. Then one mam is coming to me.

I am question to man.

Excuse me? could I help the direction for me?

The man looks like ugly face to me, and passing my side,

I am longtime oneself in thinking. And I going near store, there is sailing the fish and dry fish,

I am one more question store's boss.

Could I ask to the directions? with powerfully.

The store's boss is smiling with answering to my question.

Whatever is your any, some question to me?

I am moment doing breathe and asking to him.

I want go grocery store, could you tell me? Where is that?

The boss has fully self-confidence with smiling.

There is over there. You must have to go to left two blocks from here and that is on left conner. The boss points as fingers with detailly.

Thank you so much, sir!

The boss is smiling to me.

I am such as direction going to the that, and result have reached, I am going in grocery stores, and buying candy.

One's candy going in the mouth feeling my soul is fully with sweetly.

I was browsing the square then I was seeing one girl, the girls gathering other girls, wearing blue shirts and red scout,

I am approach to her. And I am thinking after moment. Speaking to her.

Hello?

Though I am speaking to her, she is speaking with others.

One more time speaking to him. Near approach to her.

Hello!

My name is john smith, she is look to me. And answer for question.

Hi! My name is Rola jack!

Normally calling for Rola! she is answer to that question.

I am meet to you, that is please!

Rola? how about going to browser around square?

All right! firstly, my friend introduces for you.

My side is friend is jane is my best friend. Name is jane smith.

Whoa! My first name is same me.

Next is Nancy brown, her name is Nancy brown!

She has introduced to me her friends, step by step,

We are walking for the square that is crowd with people more than more. I and her friends decide to out of the country,

We walk to go out slowly.

Hi! Rola?

Why?

How do you do your old?

I am eight old. And you?

I am seven old, next was her friend is continuously for oneself.

I have curious that and questions her.

I am going out then, street vender was speaking talk to me,

``Could I sale your breads?" as sentence is that is allows sale the breads but, if I differently listen the sentence, I am buying your beautiful, Nancy is speaking to us with smiling.

outside is beautiful flowers, weeds and little cooling windy come to front of my face, or slice passing us.

2. Be meet children.

In the morning, I am wake up early. My brother is yet sleeping.

As soon as I am rising on the bed. Wash hand and going to the kitchen and I have drinking one classes of cup. The water is dried barley made of that have boiled.

I am going out to yard. And I am playing to pick up ball, by foots kick the ball, I am stay on the head, shoulder, angle, step by sept. and running to the front. Turning left and right with ball, after latter rising the sun on the east then my eyes is brightly by sunshine. Down's morning is very clearly to me. Wetted leaves and woods are moister and cooling air come to me, freshly.

I have cleared my fore head's dews by my hand. And I am one more time playing balls. When nearly rising on the ground, I have to stop playing oneself exercise. I am going in house with out of fresh air,

Mom! I am going in.

Mother is cooking and brother is washing in the bathroom.

Father is going still outside yard carry of cows.

Father is going in the kitchen and with

speaking,

Hi daring?

Is Jany wake up?

Yes! He is his room. Now is ordering his blanket!

Jany! John! Have meal!

Yes! Father! I am going now!

I have shower and change wears and going in the kitchen, and after moment Jany is going to that. There are many foods. Table side is mother, father of front, the side is me and brother side by side.

Well, we speak the hope and have meals!

Firstly, start father! Mom is speaking to us.

Woo... I am hope that we together are happiness!

Next!

I am as brother; I hope too polite everybody.

next! Mother is speaking to me.

I hope that we are happy also. And I

hope to health mom and father,

Lastly!

At last, my mother is speaking to us, I and we hope to us healthy and happy.

We carefully eat meals,

Mom takes meals on plate for me. I have eaten bread with apple jam. And drinking one glass of milk.

In the morning sunshine go in half windows then, we finished meal nearly, father is going out to work, and Jany is going to the school, and I am helping mom wash plate and pork, and spoons.

And cleanly on the cycling table, and wash hand and brush teethe.

I am going to the school by oneself. Going to is very worm and I have buying ice drinker near at grocery store.

Hi! Sir? I want to buy one bottle ice drinker!

Hi! John!

But here, most of grocery is more expensive than under the country grocery. I am buying the grocery is my big decides.

Here, let us browser that!

I am selecting one with blue color's bottle.

How much is it?

It is seven hundred won.

Could you give me discount? I am requestioning to him.

John! how much you want discount?

One hundred won! I am speaking to him.

How about you fifty?

I will discount for you! Do so fifty won.

Yes! I will buy the bottle. I have decided to buy the bottle and sent the money to him. Perhaps, about six and five hundred won.

I walk for school and often in bottle being cooling water have drunken.

I am on going to the school, I seem trees with much growing leaves with shadows.

I am little fast walking of trees, as soon as there reached, I am laying under trees being reflect sunshine.

Up and down vibration being stick and leaves is feeling cooling to me. I am laying seeing over there the load, and my load is long away that have feeling.

I am resting shade under trees at moment, I am getting up at there. At same time I am listening to bird's sing songs.

From long away distance, approach to me, that' was 'fish."

Hi! Fish! First to him I was bow,

Hi! Jone! He is speaking to me, please.

How do you go to here? I am questions to fish?

I like together playing with some one!

What is your playing with some one?

I like playing is basketball.!

It is very funny!

Do you have ball?

I will borrow ball at the school.

How much do you have need play man?

About around over two men! Fish is sincerely speaking to me.

I and you and... later plus...

We long time stay on the hill, each other quietly.

once windy more blows to us and we stand up on planted green that.

We are walking to school, next was me often seeing fish.

He and I are stirring hand to the air, we each other smile with windy. Then nearly half going on rode to the school, strange sound listening to us, the sounds have ever listened. I am turning to my sight the toward.

There are viewing to me several people. I am deeming view to have that. Then I am ever seeming that one person with family,

That person was `Rola jack.'

She walks her friends doing talking seeing each other.

I am turning my sight to her at same time talking.

Hi! Rola!

She is stopping talking to the friends. And seeing me.

Me finding and face with please seeing me.

Oh! John!

Little short soundly is very largely feeling for me.

Their all view towards to me.

Nice meet you!

I have questions that you are going to.

She is answering to me. she has responsible that she is going to playground at school.

Among is jane also. Jane has a dark brown hair and is very more activity level than other friends, and jane is many friends being same older,

Rola is chamming. Around whom is people is speaking kindly and listening to hers.

Could going to with us, I am asking to them as gently.

Most of them are allowing to me that.

We each other bow and each with walking to the school.

After moment current time. Lora is question me about that going school.

Where are you going that?

I am playing going that!

What is you do play?

I am playing basketball!

I have not basketball, but I will borrow that from school.

Will you borrow to whom?

May be from exercise teacher or other teachers.

Maybe we play basketball for short

basketball stand shall be in school playground.

Jane and I go on talking about that playing game.

Could I join a playing?

Yes! No problem!

How much joining our paying game?

May be three!

But it is problem. If all sum is five. One is over.

Jone is concerning about joining game playing member count.

After moment, Jone is thanking problem resolvent. last one is.

that will have to judge!

Who is judge?

One of yours!

Rola is viewing to herself surround with family, then she is seeing been her next one girl.

The girls' name is Jony Logan.

She has black hair, and blue pants, it is clearly feeling code.

I am?

Yes! Are you know playing basketball?

Yes! I am little.

Jone is smiling have full pride,

I and jane decide that John have to judge.

Sommer come on little over the spring and my face go on passing by slice windy has that feeling freshly. Sun is still shining under my shoulder.

We each other walk to the school.

Jane! Could I introduce for me next is girl?

A! ah! She views to me.

I am Jody! My name is Jody.

She is kindly smiling to me. she is normal to me, and she also have dark brown color's hair.

Nice meet you! With speaking to her and.

Little later she hands over her hand to me.

Glad meet you! With speaking to her, I am grabbing her hand.

We have fully please.

Nearly reached the school. There are people still do play football and here and there are playing,

Basketball ground is playground conner is empty.

One of them is speaking to John.

Who is going to teacher?

Each other browser face at moment.

Then Nancy is speaking to us.

Could I go to the teacher to borrow basketball?

Most of them feel allowed to do.

Nancy is running to the storage of goods' room.

There is one person, old is about thirty, wearing white shirts and blue pants. May be management teacher.

Could I ask to help me, Nancy has approach to him.

The teacher is browsing to me for long. And he is speaking to her.

Of course! How can I help you?

I want to need basketball! I am sincerely responsible.

No problem, he is responsible that. And he gets a file and sit chair and speaking to me.

What your name?

My name is Nancy brown!

Could you tell me that is aim this is borrow ball?

Me be, aim is doing playing game with my friends.

The management teacher writing the list on the white board and taking the ball in the cabinet.

I am bowing to him and, picking ball and go out the room.

As likely, in the sky is white, blue color and slice windy come me care. Nancy have bounded the ball on the ground.

She surprises about the ball doing spring on the ground, then she has reached the gathering people. One person speaking to me.

Please? Could I lend me the balls?

For a moment, I will let it be touch that.

The man has thankful to me and touch my basketball.

The ball did reach to the sky and downing to the ground as soon as he has controlled the direction. The person of face is fulling smile.

At time, Nancy is thanking have to back my friends.

Hi guy!

Could you send me ball?

The man participates in touch ball.

He is not listening my voice. And I ask

to him that please!

Sent me ball?

I am getting the ball!

On the ground and ball are each other mixed that is fully dusty.

After moment, the man has sent me ball with thankful.

Nancy picks up ball and went to my friends. Cleanly blow come to me as feeling my breath to be freshly.

Nancy takes out candy that stayed in pocket and throw in her mouth.

Nancy is fully smile with sweetly taste.

Eventually. She has arrived her friends,

Jone is approach her and speaking to her.

why do you lately here?

I have come here on I am meeting one person.

The man is temporary borrow my ball and be lately.

Nancy is speaking to me and go in gathering.

Let us begin playing! Nancy talking to

gathering.

How do we share teams? One of us is speaking to me.

How about you share people to men and women.

That is good suggestion!

One of us speaking to me.

How about you each other share one's man and women are one team. And other is,

I will choice last suggestion is good to me.

Nancy browsers my friend as one by one, and decision.!

We moment rest under the tree be shade by shining.

Windy blowing from east to west.

John is speaking to us,

Let us begin game!

I and jane are one team, and Nancy and fish are one team.

We have playing game with each other please.

John hardly has judged the game.

In the sky still shinny that we play the basketball game in conner of ground.

Jane here pass! nancy speaking to me.

I have escaped from attack by fish. And I get it and throw the ball in to the basketball goal, and the ball is in that.

I and Nancy are incredibly pleased.

3.Let us go there.

In the morning, I am wake up early. Yesterday I was thinking doing playing with friends. I am hurry up have meal and go out house's back yard.

I have to resting on near house, and I am seeing to plants growing on yard,

I am sitting on wood chair and my head toward to down on ground, sometime windy blowing to my face.

Near living friend is dooly. He sometime plays with me. he is ridiculously cute and hansom. With him often I am playing with paper tag and playing with ball.

Nancy often takes apples and give him. He has likely that eaten apples.

We curious that. what is it over there? We have been going to small mountains that my house is back that

I am going and back, but over there is not going.

Perhaps. There is that will be the strange world!

We same thinking in mind.

Dooly! See over there. I am point out over there mountains.

He and I see to birds have blue color's wing flying into the sky.

Hi! Nancy?

Could I ask to you about ways going to over mountains,

May be there is wild roads and forests,

Such ours likely man is not going to there. If we go there, we will be dead or will lost road backing home.

For long time silent, and seeing the mountains,

Could you question about there?

Is man living?

May be living man in the forest.

I am speaking to him.

Nancy and dooly is each other sitting on wood chair and seeing same direction that is over mountains.

Windy is passing to us as coolly.

Sunshine still is beam to us.

We stand up wood chair, and we walk with together, his one hand grabbing ball.

Hi! Dooly?

Hi!

I am taking to candy in my pocket, and give him,

He is so happy to see for me. dooly's mouth is moving to up and down, and sometime listening sounds in mouth mixed,

Hi! Nancy?

I like calling for you, my sister!

No problem! I will be everyday you allow call me that.

I am one year elder than him. I will be friend and will be elder sister.

Now! We are sharing time!

Could you have lunch now in my house?

Little later, dooly is thinking about

that,

All right! Sister!

We go in my house each other with handing.

Mom! neighborhood is it!

All right!

Hi! Dooly!

My mom is speaking to him.

Nancy! just moment please!

I am right now! I do make it!

Mom is doing dish. I and dooly are

waiting for meal.

We each other speaking with one's thinks.

We are talking about mountain after we are going to bathroom, and washing face and hand, and going in the kitchen, sitting chair.

My mom almost made foods is variety meal, kimbap, hamburger, chicken, so on.

Mom? what is today?

No!

Do not special day, it is normal day!

Dooly is surprised that made for foods,

My mom is do not once day, sometimes it made for me.

Latter! Do so happy be that...

Dooly is freely pleased, so do I ...

Dooly picks up firstly hamburger. And has eaten that one bite and dip drink milk.

Mom is seeing him with smile.

And third is kimbap.

He is picking it and one slice bit go in

his mouth, and his face with fulling as delicious,

Dooly, it goes in, and cry for mom as thank you sir!

Last is chicken, I and he ate share meals, and I eat one cake of chicken and one more. So do dooly.

After long time passing, I and he are very fulling have eaten the meals.

Mom! thank you very much for reserve foods for us!

Mom is connecting smile to my front.

I and dooly have finish meal and go out to my house' back yard,

I and dooly are resting under shade tree by sunshine.

Then windy blow come here. That is waving my dark brown's hairs. One more time cooling windy come to us,

I and he are laying on the flat yards. And both arms have stretching to on the heading.

I am laying on the seeds that is rising plant's small is entrancing through to in my nose. I am feeling freshly and comfortable and cleanly, long away is white bule color's birds is one by one flying to their destination. And I am thinking that I will go to the over there the mountain.

Dooly is quietly close the eye, I am do not moving and seeing the sky.

Dooly?

Dooly is quietly responsible to my question.

Are you sleeping? Dooly?

Are you curious over there the

mountain?

Yes! I am!

Could we go to there?

I have to go there, but there is dangerous to me. because most of us do not go there.

We know that nearly nobody goes there!

If we go at there. Mabe to us will be dangerous.

Dooly is concern that.

I am thinking that in mine `` I will go

to there."

We step by step laying on the seed. And seeing coming person.

We see the strange man and talking stopped.

After moments, he is sitting by us. And speaking to us.

Hello! My name is Jordan max!

I am to tell you about that you ever seen around is one's sheep.

Dooly is carefully answering that question.

Yes! I am saw the sheep is almost one hundred miter distant from here, before ten minutes

The Jordan is kindly one more question to me.

Could you tell me that you seeing? where is that going to?

Over there hill!

Dooly have pointed the direction by his figure.

He is fully understand dooly talking about that. And having bow and hurry up leave the place.

I am seeing him, motionlessly.

He has going away around place is unnamed seeds slice vibration.

Windy is blow to me quietly.

Hi dooly?

Why?

If we go that there is mountain, what is reserving that us get there?

Maybe we have to foods and drink, and map of this area.

And something,

Dooly is question to her.

Who are going with?

Whom?!...

Dooly? could you go there with me?

No problem!

And you and me and with fish and other friends.

May be from five to six.!

Could I ask to them?

I am speaking to him with sincerely.

Dooly is moment thinking that and speaking to me.

How do you meet to speak that?

Maybe if I go to school and will be meet friends.

Ok! Let us begin the planning start.

Dooly and I are toward to the school.

Nancy is fulling to hope with the thinking that will have go the adventure to mountain. Her walking to the school is lightly as birds is flying to the one's home.

Nancy and dooly go on, each other smiling sometime.

Finally, they arrive at school playground, there is still many people doing rest, and playing game, and togethering.

I am taking long time researching my friends.

I see the ground conner, but I am not finding, and I see the stand stair that being cement.

Jone and fish is each other talking about something. They at same time seeing to us and have responsible.

Hello! Nice meet you.

There is my familiar in eyes, and I going there, rightly Jone is with fish.

Hello! Everyone!

How do you talk about that?

I am curious that and question to fish.

Fish is fulling with smile and speaking to me.

When we before have meal at the Jone's house. we have talking about that.

The meal was unbelievably delicious.!

At later, I will have invited Jone at my

home.

There is no other childrens, and I question to him.

Here is nobody, could you tell me who is here?

Fish and Jone are speaking to me, at same time.

But I do not understand the word, and fish one more time to tell me.

Rola is playing with their friends over there.

I am and dooly running to Rola and

she is greeting with smile to me.

Hi! Rola! nice meet you.!

Hi! glade meets you! Nancy?

I am fine thanking you. And you?

Fine thank you, Rola!

Who is there?

He is dooly. Dooly smith!

Hi! dooly?

Nice a meet you?

Nice meet you. Too!

Dooly and I and Rola are each other

having introduce on conner at playground,

Rola and dooly are more bright face,

Rola near was friends bow us, each other introduce.

I am speaking to her about trip.

Rola is curious me about that.

Could you go to the mountain, Rola?

What is say?

I and dooly like to ride mountain!

What is name of mountain?

It is my country' back mountain over is that. Name is Clarence!

Why are you going to mountain?

Why is I and dooly is curios that, I and dooly do not going to the mountain.

I and dooly have early decided that.

How about going to the mountain?

I love it because that is interesting to me, but I am thinking one more time to go to mountain.

I speaking to them. Could you go with us the mountain?

We are going to the mountain is not now, on several day remaining to the thinking.

Rola and her friends are interesting that going the clarence,

One of them speaking to me.

To going that how reserve to us?

May be, you have to titling having code, you must have drink and you have gotten to the meal, that meal is that you get for three days. And you get to have to sleeping tent.

Are you understand?

Nancy is speaking to the surround Rola's friends.

One of them is speaking to the Nancy,

If my mom is rejection that, how do we do?

This time is first. If You are going to the ride mountain, you have forgiven to me and

Let it to be back home.

Nancy and dooly is each other smiling to the Rola and her friends.

We are resting under three and

talking with me about the reserve come on ahead.

One houre latter, I, and friends back to their house.

I am remaining on the playground and thinking coming soon about riding mountain.

I am first starting to the mountain, my mine is excited,

I am standing up on the ground. I am walking to my home.

On going. I have often rested to the bench.

Tree shade is flapping by strong windy. Black color's forms be original forming, or scatter shade forming, sometime trash of one piece went to here and there on the ground.

Passing my front cute children is playing with wooden chopsticks have stirring here and there on the side road.

After moments, his mom on back seeing come on him, and his hand holding go to the direction.

The children are speaking to his mom.

Mom! please, go slowly to the direction.

The children and his mom disappear long away,

One more time blow to my face.

 I am grabbing one piece of cand and through in my mouth.

My mouth is fulling with sweetly and please.

As soon as be coming, then spraying the taste in my mind with sweetly.

Dooly is going and backing here my

sitting in place, have with breads and milks.

Could you with me share a meal?

Dooly is small's money and it buy by money. But do not appear the him self's mind, dooly is speaking to me.

These breads and milks are very fantastic for my health.

Long for hesitate, and I have decision.

Dooly carries on me the meals, which I am having eat.

Dooly? Please give me the meal. I will

have pay that is prices.

Okey! Nancy!

But you do not' pay to the meals' prices.

I am very thankful about that, in mind is fulling with thankful.

One more time passing the people, and we have eaten the meals.

The surround benches have crowded with peoples. We have all sum and at bench we had sitting, rising on place. and we are walking on the street,

After two and three days, we will go to the mountain, and I and dooly will reserve the meals and riding mountain's need usages.

Usage is shoes, and wears and water, and meals, bag, and luggage are we have gotten them.

Dooly and I am nearly reaching to the house. and we each other have farewell.

I am going in the house, and I speak to my mom!

Mom! I am going in now.!

My voice is eco to me,

I am going to back yard, there is my mom is at there.

Hello! Mom?

Mom's forehead is fulling with sweats. And her wear is wetting with mixed toils and water.

Mom! I am going here.

Hi! Nancy! Could you help me?

Mom is fixing gas boiler.

How can I assist you?

I hope you have sent me the tools.

Have me?

I am hurry up grab tools and passing them.

Thank you! Nancy!

Mom? what's problem that is?

Maybe... gas boiler's stove pipe has been blocking!

I am curious that, and more have question to mom.

How long you will do fixed that?

Mom participates in fixing that. After moment, have responsible to my question,

Maybe, about thirty minutes.

Nacy is seeing to mom's fixing boiler.

Nancy? Could give me brush? Why? Mom?

I have to clean surround fixing that.

Ok! Mom!

Nacy is taking the brush to the left conner.

Thank you daring!

Dusted mom's face is fulling with gentle, plus with smile.

Mom is finishing that repair, going the kitchen, and take have juice to me.

Juice have fulling with grained oranges.

I am receiving the orange on side hands, eating on I had do two or three split side in place.

Mom is question to me.

How about you have dinner?

Mom! not yet!

I will have to playing be outside.

That is no problem! My cute!

Mom is responsible and go in the kitchen.

I am ordering my room and go to the back yard,

There is suite to me only alone playing.

Because I like the place is normal size to playing.

Near is narrow water and small mountain. Sometime coming on to me, birds is flaying both wings up and down.

I am getting in the warehouse to picking the hoe.

I am purpose to riding mountain, and picking the that and I am going backyard of middle and digging the small size hole to ahead to set tent. Firstly, ever I have not tried to be setting the tent, but that be little likely to see for me.

My forehead is sweat rising little more with water drop.

She is face as fulling with smiling in mind.

My wear is wetting with sweat, and I am stopping the exercise about digging medium size hole, I am thinking that have to rest under tree, I go to the bench near my house be plants on the ground. The bench did make of woods have to be comfortable to me.

Sometime blowing me chilly wind, which did me having cool, to my forehead,

Then I am seeing the sunshine beaming to me.

Having Little worm to me.

Nancy!

In the house my mom is calling me through windows and listening sound.

I am here, mom! I am crying to my mom to windows.

Nancy! have a meal!

Yes! Mom! outside air is more and more worm. And windy come me side with cooling.

I am set hoe in warehouse, and I am walking slowly to my home,

Out of the back yard is remaining that I have digging the hole on the grounds.

I am going to my house and wash hand and face and exchange my wears. Then come on mom's speaking to me.

Nancy!

Have you will do not go out now?

Yes! Mom! I will do not go out!

I am responsible that and have meals.

Then I am sitting down, my mom is still busy.

On My table sets on one class of milk

and bread.

I have one bite of breads and little drinking of milk.

Nancy! Could I ask to you doing outside?

Yes! Mom!

What is your digging hole outside?

aha! I am plaining going that to the mountain.

The mountain name is clearance.

I am pride of the noun to speaking to my mom.

Nancy! The mountain is barely living men.! Mom is speaking to me with smiling.

So, I do know that, but I want seeing over there,

With whom you going there?

Yet I do not decide that.!

Mabe, I and fish, Rola, Jone are going with together.

Could I help you reserve?

I am reserve meal, wears, tent, Nancy tells her mom.

I will do reserve meal for you. Okey?

When do you leaves to mountain?

That is certainly did not decide that!

I will tell you after deciding that!

Each other speaking to that after I am going up the chair, go in my room,

That stair is making of wood, and often listening sound as rising stair.

Then I am staying my room, mom's sing song listening to me.

Mabe mom is kitchen likely.

I am writing in my daily plane

notebook to which is reserving about supplies.

After writing reservation supplies, I am moment sleeping of.

Outside is my mom is calling to me.

Nancy!

I am hearing the sounds is finding for me.

Mom! I am here!

I am responsible and go directly to my mom.

What's matter mom?

A minute ago, I am fixing boiler is do not well.!

I have to calling neighborhood.

Nancy! Please! Do you have stay home?

Yes! Mom! I will do now.

I am listening that My mom is closing door' sound.

I am going the kitchen and biting one of cookie that is sweetly.

One more that I am as eating as feeling in taste is delivering in my mind as comfortable.

I am dancing with a creak of wood floor.

One step, and two step, and more step...

After moment, my mom is taking with neighborhood's uncle is brown, mom is straight calling me.

Yes! Mom!

Mom is exam the boiler with him.

Him is having sideburn and medium size body, and face was likely seeing comfortable.

Mom and uncle are talking about boiler. I am near chair by the table.

My mom is little disappointed that change boiler.

Mom is serving one class of juice to him.

Thank you so much you come here!

My mom is bow him,

Uncle has come out my home.

Mom is concerning about fixing boiler.

I am going straitly to my room,

I have unfolded the book and have start reading book.

After two passing, I am going down in the kitchen.

Always there was my mom. mom have doing dish.

Mom! I am hungry!

I am speaking to mom,

Just moment please!

I made the dish! going out.! Mom speaking to me with confidence.

Yes!

Mom? could I ask to you that?

What is that?

Mom is concerned that.

Maybe, I will buy the boiler! Mom is speaking to me with smile.

Do not worry about that!

Ok! Mom!

The window is often vibration by windy.

Mom?

Why!

Could I ask to you that's house?

No problem that!

How old this house? I am doing seeing up in the house.

May be, this house has been thirty years old.

Mom? could you tell me about that this house did be sale.

I and your father are earning, and the money saving and finally have buying this house.

Before this house is normal, but now

is many things have to repair, stairs, doors, windows, water pipeline, even if boiler, so on.

I will have to plans to repair the house, example, I am writing a diary to repair the house. step by step fixing the house,

Nacy is involving her mom's eyes, with bright shining,

Mom! so do I.

I will plain daily have to works in the note will be writing that,

Mom and I are talking about that, I am going to my bedroom. Near window is shining warm air by the sunshine.

I am sitting on the chair and do be plan the ride up mountain.

If we have meet each other, we have to will be talking about that.

Her sitting chair is more than more worms be to her in mind with comfortable.

4.We gather in my house to be planning to go to mountain.

On afternoon, quietly the windy is booming to the windows.

That then, I am wake up, stretching my arms to my head,

Mom is kitchen always, I am going to bathroom to wash face,

And I am reaching there then, my mom is fixing the water pipe,

Mom! I am hungry.

Oh! Nancy! What I do that for you?

Mom! I want eating meal!

Ok! I will reserve meal for my cute.

Just moment please!

Mom is fixing the water pipe that taking thirty minutes.

The long for, I was sitting on floor on

aside the ground made by wood.

Mom is fixing after, I am going in my bathroom, and washing hand, and face,

My mom is hurry going in the kitchen. Then I am washing body.

After moment. Mom is calling for me.

My cute! Have meal!

Yes! Mom! I am going in the kitchen.

In the kitchen is forth leg. One is normal. Two is slice normal, the last is a little broken leg got fixing.

On the table is bread, soup, spoon, and fork.

Have delicious!

As soon as I am dipping breads yellow soup, I have going in my mouth. Sweetly is widely in mind with sweetly.

Out of windows, I listen to me dogs barking sounds.

As I am eating one piece of breads, listen to me dogs' sing song. As it is mixing sweetly and comfortable, have full be please.

Could you more eating?

Yes! Please!

Mom is purring a soup in my front of bowl.

Thank you, mom!

Could you give me one more bread?

Mom is consistently smiling for me.

Mom handed on to me one more one piece of bread in small plate. Mom! thank, you!

In the mouth with mixed bread and soup send to me feeling very sweetly.

Mom hand me napkin, I am cleanly

scraps around in my mouth.

After moment, I am getting up my chair listening sounds as vibration oneself. That is as soon as sitting on the chair, risen the noise.

I am one more bit one piece and eat one spoon's soups.

My face is fulling the please.

Mom! thank you have meal!

I am directly going to bathroom and face wash and brash my teeth, mom is cleaning dishes and going in her room.

So do I am going my room,

I am thinking the plane about riding mountain, I am sitting on the chair and one hand is gapping a pencil and I am writing down on the paper,

The firstly, how many people is participant, and reserve of foods to the numbers, and we have to getting the tents.

Adequately.

She is pick up the paper and folding and through in the pocket.

Outside is still brightly by the sunshine.

She is walking slowly on the road, sometime windy come to me be slice booming,

I am toward to the school playground, there is often seeing children than before.

I am seeing here and there, but nobody is family to me.

About 30-minute waiting then, one girl come to me. the girls nearly reached to me!

Hi! Nancy!

Oh! Hi Rola!

Rola was wearing white shirts, seen such a very shape. And she is very clearing.

What do you do here?

I am to see my friends, likely such you.

Why do you meet to us?

I have to telling you about riding mountain.

How do you think to going the mountain?

I am asking to Rola.

I am interesting for waiting that go to the mountain.

The firstly for me,

I have curiosity for me that going up mountain.

After I am born, it will be newly for me the experience.

Who do you go with?

Maybe, john and me and Jack, Rola! I will be thinking that one and two is more.

How do you thinking about taking us with that?

May be, basically, you have to personal tool, meal, wear, and

Emergency gears and Madison so on...

Rola and I are talking about that,

Windy was coming here from west to east, in the sky still currency small and ugly clouds current up our heads.

After moment, nearly 20 minutes later, long away stranger come here with vaguely.

Who is he?

Long away two's people come to us,

More than more approach to us.

Hi! Nacy! And Lola!

Nice meet you! Everybody?

Come here that men are jack and john.

Among us is each other doing handshake with smiling,

Lately autumn's sky is still clearly with cooling windy.

We are together walking to Nacy's house.

Nacy and Rola and john and jack and lastly is dooly.

We side by sidewalk for the Nancy's house, each other having hand on.

Rola! could you hand me the box?

Ok! Here there are!

Nancy? What is it in?

My books are in!

It is the map about we are around staying area!

It will open the box if we are reaching the house.

I am seeing face each other with her,

We take twenty minutes to be there.

Nacy's house is empty, mom has out town to buy grocery.

Rola is open the door quietly, then two's dog come out and

Barking to us. At moment, being silence around.

Them of one is seeing me involving with one' nose is currenting snot.

I am taking out candy in my pocket and through the candy to long away yard.

Two dogs running to the yard and find candy and have eating that. I and friends go in the house.

I am going in my house and walking through the passage and reach front door then open the door care and have seeing to me clearly and orderly sciences.

I am thinking that, maybe my mom is herself have doing that.

In the kitchen is meal desk and chairs have clearly.

I am sitting with friends on the chair.

And take out map book from my box.

Friends see that with sincerely.

The maps are detailed expression this area.

Could you tell me where are start point?

May be this is pointing start will be!

I am carefully this area has pointing,

The area has doing flat to the ground

and little, and small trees,

Entrance is narrow road that is surround each other is small lakes.

Each other we are talking about reserving that have to reserve tools and meals, tents,

We are walking for Nancy's house each other.

Nancy and I am walking with each other, but I am handy my hand to her, quietly, I am giving to her smiling,

Nearly, we have reach Nancy's house,

Front of yard, two's dogs come here with tale swing left and right. And they are barking to us with smiling.

I am explanation my friends that one is mane is blue and other is jam.

Almost We have doing reaches the house .and go in the house.

Hi mom!

Nancy cry to mom.

Mom is giving us with quietly.

Thank you, sir!

Friends bow to the Nancy's mom, one

by one,

Hi sir! my name is dooly!

Hi sir! my name is john!

Next, jack is bowing to her. And jack is doing to her.

And Nancy's friends go in the house,

Nancy's house is little worn but most of is very clearly.

Most of one is question Nancy' mom.

Could I sit down here?

No problem!

Nancy's mom is cool allow for that.

We are sitting around table, and mom give us six classes of juice.

We all sometimes have bow to the Nancy's mom.

Mom! thank you very much! We will be doing delicious!

Mom's face is full of amazing.

Mom has meal with them.

From ahead in cycling meal desk to last, Nancy, jack, john, dooly, and Rola are sitting on chairs.

Nancy! Could you tell me your mother is name?

Nancy! Responsible that.

My mother's name is Rollen!

Hi Rollen! I like question about this house?

No problem john!

This house is ten years old, it is old,

Rollen is carefully speaking to him.

One more question her.

But I have seen the house is cleaning. Maybe I do not think.

that is old this house.

how do you manage this house?

this house is managed one day per one week by oneself.

Mom is responsible the question and get up the chair and go to front of the range.

Rollen is taken on the plate that many and variety food and that getting on table, one by one,

Hi john?

Yes! Rollen!

How would you like to kind of meal?

I like that no reason!

Maybe I have to eating that everything. Maybe exception I do not eating.

Well!

Could you eat that I do make it oneself.

Rollen is sent to him on the plate that making bread with cream.

The bread is sweet to me,

Mom gives me the same johns that.

Next is jack and ...

On the table full of variety color, and in the kitchen is full of worm air.

Nancy's friends with being brightly face and have delicious that mom is cooking.

 Outside is still slice cold.

We talk about important riding mountain. Firstly, we are thinking riding mountain, but we are thinking the mountain, we decide to have to exploring mountain.

We have gone with reserved tools

oneself is decide,

Hi Rollen!

Could you once more give me one class of juice?

Mom is smiling to her.

No problem dooly!

She takes out bottle and pure in my class.

In grass full of yellow color. Dooly drinking that. And with

Fulling sweetly, her face is smiling to Rollen,

we in the night go back their home...

in the dark blue sky is still brightly yellow color...

5.Only their adventure is starting with us.

The day is now.

Nancy and dooly meet under the steep hill connected to village. The area with covered gravel, toile is mixed on the ground.

Nancy is having heavy luggage and because in that is the tent.

After passing one house, john is coming from away,

john is speaking to dooly.

Hi! dooly!

Nice meet you! John?

John is approach them. And they cross hand over to be shake hand.

Autumn winds is coming booming on my face.

Sometime passing sounding rise birds and pets' crying to me.

John is speaking to dooly.

Why is jack doing late?

Maybe jack will be soon coming!

We are talking about jack then. Long away seen to me that is.

Jack wearing blue and red suits.

Jack swing hand to us with please,

Perhaps, ten meters approached to us then,

Jack seen to us shapely form,

Hi! jack!

How are you doing late here?

I am reserved various tools as likely method. And I am getting up lately.

Nancy and dooly is smile to him,

We gather each other spot in place and sitting down on the on the ground with green seed growing greenly.

Jone is taking out the map in the pocket. And set on the ground.

And speaking to us.

We now are here; john is pointing as his finger. We involve his finger.

Forehead, we have to gone is here,

Rightly now, I am seeing to mountain that is snow cover with cold and being grand.

Hi john! Dooly is question to him with sincerely.

How long be taken to walk for us doing resting?

Maybe, one houre walk per one resting, resting have to take twenty minutes.

John is folding the map and take in his backpack.

We walk to prospecting area spot, their shoes are not perfect but that is normal to us rising mountain,

Surround is fully of sounds with variety bird's crying to me.

We are walking to the forest and covering with woods on the head,

Dooly is singing by oneself, that is his favorite song.

The back is jack so did that.

Morning shine is doing beam to us warmly.

After two minutes, one of us is speaking to john, with tired,

Right, that is Nancy,

Are we resting now? I am tired now.

We little more walk for twenty miters.

We find that we are resting that over there is flat place,

The spot is cycling shadows by woods' blocking to hot shining.

We rest for moment, Nancy! Are you ok?

John questions to her,

Her face is dewing of water.

I am ok! now! Nancy is smiling to him. Nancy's hand with scarf is browsed her head forward. After moment, slice wind is passing to us,

Hi! john!

Where are we doing take for the spot?

I am now eating food!

Dooly is speaking to john.

John is thanking that moment,

Yes! But, you have not to throw trash.

We have to prevent nature.

If we throw the trash. We will be meet wild animals with having too wildly.

John is kindly explained to him.

Dooly, he turns his head and doing forehead, his front of head, about two miters, small bird siting and crying song with peacefully is seen to us.

John is taking candys in his pocket and one is had oneself and others is given them.

We rise on the spot, start walking for the place.

Nancy is full of comfortable,

All are no comment each other, and quietly working.'

Sometime listening to waterline in the depth currenting sound,

And sometime seen to me squirrel running and holding foods by their teeth and passing us front.

I am Nancy is side by side walking

with handy.

We decide slowing walking for Nancy.

Maybe, we are plaining as lately about ten minutes, which is john's thinking about.

One more time, anyone is singing song,

who is jack!

If each other singing, we will be lively, and one more step, being mine is lightly.

John is turning his head to seeing one

more mountain. But do not see because that is cover as woods shades, only listening birds sounds,

We are going about ten minutes then we reached the spot.

And john is carefully taking map and examining on that, this.

Place is formal for us, john is the same thinking, this place is.

Perfect spots that we are going up to the mountain.

Well, john is decided taking to resting about that thirty minute.

John is taking candy in his pocket,

The candy is sweetly to him in his mouth with happy.

Hi! john!

Could you eat someone?

There is meal, which is kimbap is my mom is reservation for me.

Thank you, Nancy!

I was pass to her and I was bit one piece of kimbap.

What is made of material? Suddenly, their sight forward to jack.

Jack is taking out bread and milk from his pack.

Personally, we are seen to us is simple but, that is special,

Other person is easily learning money but, his mother is hardly learning money with labor, buying the food, giving him for that.

More, the bread is specially made in that.

Rising in the early morning. His mother in person makes that as well as, his family all are make for him.

Could you eat meals?

Jack is taking meals in his backpack. And that share per one piece, then dooly is rising hand.

I like to only one piece.

Jack is smiling to dooly and sending to him.

Each other have to little amount of food.

John is taken map his backpack.

We that are doing reaching the aim point spot have been to

Complete, firstly is easily, but we do not know about approach work.

We walk to the next spot place, we were backing the place, and we go to the ahead, slowly,

John is one more take out map in his backpack,

Hi! john!

Where are we going to?

Dooly is question to john.

Maybe, we have to walk about one hour.

Now. This road is wild, and we have to walking carefully.

Suddenly, right direction is birds passing fast through on our head. Then Nancy is surprised by that,

Nancy? Ok?

No problem! Nancy is responsible about john's question.

Woods and seeds to be meet by sun are smelling freshly feeling.

We were fulling with shrill and curious about this riding to the

Mountain,

Nancy, john, and jack and dooly, and,

We go there, sometime rode side is a flat rock likely sitting that we are resting on that.

Surround area we are walking covered with shade by woods is very cooling to us.

After passing twenty minutes, Nancy is calling to him.

Could I rest here?

John is responsible for the question.

Yes! You can! But if within twenty we take to go there, we will reach our destination.

We have decided to rest near places.

I am sitting on shaded flat ground and examining near surround area. I am definitely that the area is safe.

Nacy is doing her ahead with dew.

Hi! john!

Could you responsible my question?

No problem!

John is responsible about that!

How take we are going there? to we are plain the place that reach.

Mabe, we are late about one hour, john is responsible that.

Sometime, cool windy to in my cloth blow slice cooling.

The place We will be to going is slice deep yard, and we there will be eating for lunch.

Nacy and I have resting at near wood and be quietly surround.

Surround is listening pets' crying to us.

John takes out candy in his pocket and through in his mouth,

Sweely is full in his mouth.

Passing twenty minutes, we get up on the ground and have starting walking to the destination,

As soon as We are going there, birds are following us and sing songs,

It is now, deep road seen to us, we little tension about that,

But passing moment, flat rode seen to us,

Small shiny is reflected near narrow waterline brightly seen to us.

One more time, little distant for me, jack's shoelace come untied, and my sight towards jack, and...

Jack! Your shoes!

Jack' his sight towards to the down.

With Jack's heavy backpack, he is doing down his head, and one more having tide his light shoelace.

Often his shoelace come untied,

The clarence is not nearly living in that.

And no one known about that, only eye seeing that cover snow and deep line 's cliff, there, we have going now,

We are passing narrow road, and we walk about four miters, we see the wetlands, that wetland is anyone did not pass that,

I and Nancy and we are slowly walking for ahead. As soon as I am footing on ground, after any second the footage has appeared, and our foot have been wetted by wetlands' moister.

I am going to ahead on anybody call

me, rightly. Nacy is on wetlands, her foot's ankle is fulling in the water and toile are mixed.

She has crying to us.

Can I help me? fall into wetlands!

The then, dooly go to the slowly and her hand grappling and side by side, walking for ahead.

Nancy also crying for us.

I want to back home!

Her eye is small dewing water.

We have passed the wetlands,

All their shoes were wetted as toil and water are mixed, and their walking was little heavy.

Nacy! Are you ok?

I am ok now, but I am afraid go ahead. But now well.

John is taking candy in his pocket and sent to her.

Anywhere listening sound to us, that is dooly's singing song.

We are singing song together,

Still birds follow us with singing song.

As soon as passing wetlands, that seen to me wild road is doing nothing plants, we carefully walking the narrow road, as soon as by one step, I am feeling a hard.

John is taking out map in his backpack, and that lifting and going near quietly under shade of woods.

We all follow him and sitting down on flat ground.

 John! dooly question him.

We are well going now.

Yes!

John is responsible that, and carefully opening the map by side hands.

John involved examining the map.

One more question to him.

John! How much reached the destination we have lunch?

Maby after one hour will be passing by then.

One more getting up on the ground and started walking a head.

We pass the forest and hotter sunshine beams to us. Dooly and I am connecting drinking water, and quietly hand over bottle to jack.

Jack receives the bottle and drinking water and pass the bottle to Nancy.

Nancy?

Are you ok?

Do well than before!

Be hotting Sunshine is drying my shoes.

We are slowly walking ahead.

We surround come still slice cool windy,

Dooly is charging firstly aid medicine, and we are all is safe.

Now, we walking to the destination as doing place tent.

Hi! dooly I am ancle ache now!

Could you help me?

Jack is stuck by walk passing wood's stick.

Jack's ancle has little hunter, and there are little rising bloods.

Are you okey?

After having disinfection, Dooly wind

up band on his angle.

They are walking after pass thirty. They find dead woods of dem in area.

Surround is dark and cooling, we are carefully walking for ahead also my head turns down, on the rode is narrow and wetted by moister, side the wood seen to me quietly aimed with gloomy.

We are walking to the ahead with carefully as one by one,

The birds are Passing me that we have not known that suddenly come here us is,

About twenty minutes, then surrounded mountain, so darkness,

We are going to dark area and doing in fall.

More and more we are going to ahead, surrounds are dark with covering mountain's shade is blocking sunshine.

We pass the dead's woods and after thirty minutes later, our destination nearly has reached.

We have reach destination is there is that we have resting area is not. And we decide more walk to the front narrow road.

Narrow road passing, which seen to me the place.

We are rising both hands, and crying to mountain,

Hi! Nancy!

Could you help me the tent roading on the load?

We place the tent on the spot with each other.

John is speaking to us.

We will have name here is calling as basic point.

John and dooly and jack's tent is blue color and Nancy and Rola's tent is red color.

From Starting spot distance to my country is one our distant.

We are going over there, and we have drinking water,

And washing hands and, rice is cooking on my utensil,

We reached spot areas is perfect to have resting,

John is taking the candy in his pocket, and hand in to her.

West is widely sightly to us, and the place is good place have to sleeping.

I am on more time seeing the sky is blue and clearing.

Under there mountain

발 행 :2024년 7월 23일

저 자: 김용호

펴낸이: 한건희

펴낸 곳: 주식회사 부크크

출판사등록:2014.07.15(제2014-16호)

주소: 서울 특별시 금천구 가산 디지털 1로 119 SK트윈타워 A동 305호

전화:1670-8316

이메일: imfo@book.co.kr

ISBN:979-11-410-9684-7

www.bookk.co.kr

@Under there mountain 2024